WITHDRAWN

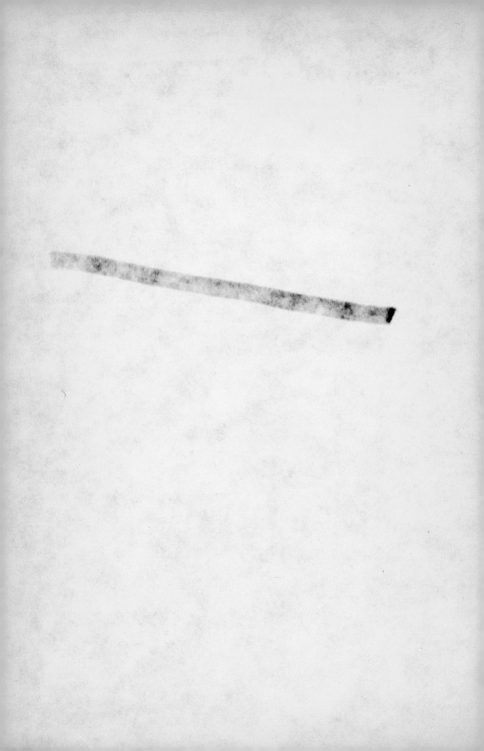

CONCERNING THE FRONTISPIECE

Because we consider "Ye Giglampz" of major importance in the early literary career of Lafcadio Hearn, we reproduce as our frontispiece the first page of the first issue of this Journal. Lafcadio Hearn and H. F. Farney published the magazine in Cincinnati, in 1874—when Hearn was twenty-four years old. In this precocious publishing experiment are to be found some of the most interesting of all attempts at satire and humor known to have been written by Hearn. *See Item No. 1 in the Checklist.*

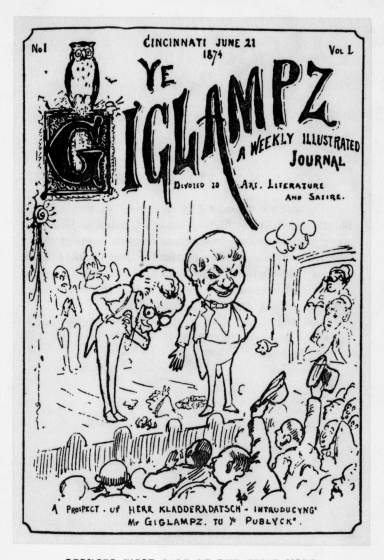

REDUCED FIRST PAGE OF THE FIRST ISSUE

LAFCADIO HEARN:
FIRST EDITIONS AND VALUES

A CHECKLIST
for COLLECTORS
by
WILLIAM TARG

(*Author of*: "The Pauper's Guide To Book
Collecting"; "999 Books Worth Reading";
"American First Editions & Their Prices").

1 9 3 5
THE BLACK ARCHER PRESS
CHICAGO

PRINTED IN THE U. S. A.

TO MY SON

RUSSELL

CONTENTS

INTRODUCTION

The present work is the outgrowth of a personal life-long interest in the writings and career of that strange phenomenon and literary genius, Lafcadio Hearn. It is impossible, after an extended acquaintance with his works, not to be enkindled with the desire to assist in making him better known to the world. To read his books is to become a proselyte. He weaves a spell of enchantment over his readers, and they become, not only devotees, but collectors. As his first editions have come to be more avidly collected, the need for a bibliographical check-list guide to his works has become apparent.

This little book is issued to serve as a handy pocket guide to collectors of Hearn; it is intended as a practical aid in buying and selling his first editions; but in no manner does it presume to be a complete bibliography. For complete collations, and for a detailed record of all printed material relevant to the subject, we refer you to that admirable work "Lafcadio Hearn A Bibliography" by P. D. and Ione Perkins, issued last year by Houghton Mifflin & Co.

Lafcadio Hearn presents one of the most colorful and fascinating subjects for the book-collector and student of literature. Though widely known, he remains as yet the object, more or less, of a cultish following. He is best known for a few works, namely "Some Chinese Ghosts", "Japan An Interpretation", "Kwaidan", and "Stray Leaves." His volumes of lectures published in Tokyo are becoming better known, and represent some of the most refreshing, scholarly and original critical writings ever offered to students of literature. Within the past ten or fifteen years, Hearn has come to enjoy universal recognition as one of the few Occidentals to succeed in acquainting us with the beauty and charm, the poetry, mysticism and wisdom of Japan. He has served as the bridge to a better and more sympathetic understanding of that country, and it is undoubtedly and gratifyingly true that he is as much beloved by the Japanese nation as he is by the English speaking people. And already one can find translations of his works as well as critical estimates of the man, in a dozen foreign languages.*

As a master of prose and poetic imagery, he remains without a peer in our literature, and certainly from the standpoint of pure originality, belongs in that coterie of literary artists which includes such stellar names as Edgar Allan Poe, Ambrose Bierce and Stephen Crane. His journalistic writings are vivid, racy—and any present-day newspaper reporter can well afford to read and study some of the magnificent news-stories Hearn wrote for the Cincinnati and New Orleans papers. His exquisite prose-poems are comparable to those of Baudelaire and Verlaine. His translations, adaptations—social, mystical and critical studies—constitute a definite and valuable contribution to our literature and the literature of the world. His position in American letters is as unique as Poe's, and, like Poe, it is but a matter

---

* The Hokuseido Press, Nishiki-cho Kanda-ku, Tokyo, recently issued a catalogue (111 pp., illustrated) containing articles and records of posthumous honors given Hearn by the Japanese and Greek governments. This catalogue should be of interest to all Hearn collectors and I am sure it can be secured upon request.

of time before Hearn's full significance will be recognized.*

A considerable amount of biographical material has already been published about Hearn,** and it is noteworthy if not amusing to recall at this time that Dr. George Gould once said of him: "Of Lafcadio Hearn there has been, and there will be no excuse for any biography whatever."! Although much has been published about the man, it is the opinion of this writer that the definitive biography of Hearn remains yet to be written. At the date of this writing, a new and most interesting volume has been issued by Kazuo Koizumi, Hearn's son. The book is entitled "Father And I" and it is a work that will help the future biographer immeasurably, because of its honesty in portraying the man Hearn as he was seen by one of his own family. Another work, "Lafcadio Hearn in Profile" by Tsutomu Takata, librarian of the Lafcadio Hearn Library in Toyama, will probably be published in English shortly.

---

* For an interesting estimate of Hearn the artist, we suggest to the reader James G. Huneker's essay, "The Cult of the Nuance", Chapter XIII, "Ivory Apes & Peacocks", N. Y., 1915.

** See BOOKS ABOUT LAFCADIO HEARN, page 45.

We present herewith a few general biographical facts: Hearn was born June 27, 1850 in Leucadia, in the Ionian Islands, of Irish-Greek parents. His father was an Irish army officer, and his mother a Greek from Cerigo. Lafcadio (named after the Island on which he was born) received some education in France and England; in 1869, at the age of nineteen—alone, friendless, and suffering from an unfortunate myopic condition—he came to America. He endured unspeakable hardship and privation, but ultimately found work on newspapers in Cincinnati and New Orleans. In 1890 he left for Japan, where he married a Japanese woman, changed his name to Koizumi Yakumo, and adopted the Buddhistic faith. Hearn lectured on English Literature at the Imperial University of Tokyo. He died September 26, 1904. Yone Noguchi said of him at his death: "He was a delicate, easily broken vase, old as the world, beautiful as a cherry blossom. Alas! That wonderful vase is broken. He is no more with us. Surely we could lose two or three battleships at Port Arthur rather than Lafcadio Hearn."

Several of Hearn's first editions offer bibliographical difficulties, and wherever to our knowledge a point of issue exists, we give it in our description. We have examined most of the books herein listed having bought and sold Hearniana consistently for the past twelve years. All titles are listed chronologically. Where the date or place of publication is indicated within brackets, for example (1898), the date is not to be found on the title page of the first edition, but elsewhere, or not at all. We have priced the books to the best of our ability, according to recent auction records and booksellers' catalogues, placing a fair average current value on each. The highest prices given are for copies in mint condition, usually where an original dustwrapper accompanies the book—and also for certain books in their scarcest bindings, for example: "Chinese Ghosts" in yellow cloth, or "Youma" in the white calico blue design-stamped binding. Several items we left unpriced as it was impossible to arrive at an approximation on books which are almost never offered for sale. We assume no responsibility in matters of prices, and can suggest only that the physical condition of a book, the supply and demand for it, together with other variable circumstances affect the price of a book. We wish to add that none of Hearn's books was originally issued in large editions, and consequently because of their limited availability, one should not hesitate to pay a fair price for any of them, especially when they are obtainable in fine condition. Many of Hearn's books were beautifully printed, illustrated and bound—according to the highest standards of fine typography and craftsmanship, and a collection of his works will afford one more aesthetic pleasure than would, say, a shelf-full of 19th Century New England poets! Thus, a Hearn collector derives manifold pleasure from his hobby for when he has become weary of reading, he may enjoy *looking* at his books!

It is the sincere hope of the compiler that this little book will prove useful to collectors and help in some degree to make Hearn's works more widely known; if, in this capacity it is successful, he will feel amply rewarded.

WILLIAM TARG

Chicago, 1935

1. YE GIGLAMPZ*. A Weekly Illustrated Journal Devoted to Art, Literature and Satire. Cincinnati, 1874. Eight numbers issued in all.

"Published daily, except week-days by the Giglampz Publishing Co., 150 West Fourth St." Each number consists of 8 pages; size 14½ x 10¾", and later 16x11¼". First published June 21st, 1874, and expired August 2nd, 1874. Anonymously published by Lafcadio Hearn and H. F. Farney, the latter contributing the drawings, and Hearn a large portion of the copy. A complete set of this Journal represents probably the scarcest of all Hearniana. See FRONTISPIECE.

Value: Inestimable

---

* Not collated in Perkins.

2. LA NOUVELLE ATALA OU LA FILLE DE L'ESPRIT. Légende Indienne Par Chahta-Ima. Nouvelle-Orleans, 1879.

Bound in various colored paper wrappers, 140 pages. This represents the first appearance of Lafcadio Hearn's work in book form.

Value: $

1882

3. ONE OF CLEOPATRA'S NIGHTS AND OTHER FANTASTIC ROMANCES. BY THEOPHILE GAUTIER. Translated by Lafcadio Hearn. New York, 1882.

Bound in red cloth. Publisher's name is stamped in caps at bottom of backbone of first issue. This is the first appearance of Hearn's name on a title page.

Value: $30-75.

4. STRAY LEAVES FROM STRAY LIT-ERATURE. Stories Reconstructed from the Anvari-Soheili, Baitál Pachísí, Máhabharata, Pantchantra, Gulistan, Talmud, Kalewala, etc. Boston, 1884.

Bound in green, blue or brown cloth, all first issues.

Value: $40-125.

1885

5. "GOMBO ZHÈBES". Little Dictionary of Creole Proverbs Selected From Six Creole Dialects. Translated Into French and Into English . . . by Lafcadio Hearn. New York, 1885.

Various colored cloth bindings, all first issues.

Value: $12-20.

1885

6. HISTORICAL SKETCH BOOK AND GUIDE TO NEW ORLEANS AND ENVIRONS. New York, 1885. With Map.

Bound in wrappers, and in blue or brown cloth. Hearn's name must NOT appear on page 299.

Value: $15-30.

7. LA CUISINE CREOLE. A Collection of Culinary Recipes From Leading Chefs and Noted Creole Housewives, . . . New York, (1885).

Various colored cloth bindings. First issue copies must have "Brùlot" NOT "Brülot" in the 9th line of the Introduction which should run one and a half pages; no lettering on backbone.

Value: $45-100.

1887

8. SOME CHINESE GHOSTS. Boston, 1887.

Various colored cloth bindings, all firsts; it is believed that the copies bound in yellow are the scarcest although there is no priority. Should have figured end-papers.

Value: $45-125.

1889

9. CHITA: A MEMORY OF LAST IS-LAND. New York, 1889.

Reddish-brown cloth binding. A portion of this story appeared previously in "Harper's Fifth Reader" New York, 1889, and was entitled "The Coming Of The Hurricane."

Value: $12-20.

10. THE CRIME OF SYLVESTRE BON-
NARD. BY ANATOLE FRANCE. Transla-
tion and Introduction by Lafcadio Hearn. New
York, 1890.

Bound in blue wrappers. Advertisement in-
side front wrapper should list "Franklin Square
Library" which must not contain titles numbered
later than No. 665 (Sylvestre Bonnard).

LARGE PAPER COPY same as above,
size 5¾x8³⁄₁₆" bound in brown cloth, with paper
label.

Value: $30-50.

Large Paper, Value: $30-60.

1890

11. TWO YEARS IN THE FRENCH WEST
INDIES. New York, 1890.

Bound in olive-green or orange cloth, with
decorations.

Value: $10-15.

12. YOUMA THE STORY OF A WEST-INDIAN SLAVE. New York, 1890.

Various cloth bindings were used for the first edition of this book, including white calico with blue design (considered earliest binding), blue and red cloth, and several mottled cloths. The red cloth copies have title in gold on spine; other bindings have paper labels.

Value: $12-20.

1894

13. GLIMPSES OF UNFAMILIAR JAPAN. 2 volumes. Boston and New York, 1894.

Bound in green or black cloth with silver stamping, the green binding being the earliest issued.

Value: $20-25.

1895

14. "OUT OF THE EAST" REVERIES AND STUDIES IN NEW JAPAN. Boston and New York, 1895.

Yellow cloth binding with silver stamping, stained top. Should measure $1\frac{5}{16}''$ thick across covers.

Value: $12-20.

15. KOKORO. HINTS AND ECHOES OF JAPANESE INNER LIFE. Boston and New York, 1896.

Bound in olive-green cloth, gold stamped.

Value: $7-12.

16. GLEANINGS IN BUDDHA-FIELDS. Studies of Hand and Soul In the Far East. Boston and New York, 1897.

Blue cloth binding with gold stamping.

Value: $10-15.

17. EXOTICS AND RETROSPECTIVES. Boston, 1898.

Green cloth binding, with decorations.

Value: $12-15.

18. THE BOY WHO DREW CATS. Japanese Fairy Tale Series No. 23. Rendered Into English By Lafcadio Hearn. (Tokyo, 1898)

Wrappers. Size 7⅛x9¾". Printed in colors by hand from wood blocks.

19. SAME: Printed on Crêpe-Paper, size 5⅜x7½". Description as above.

Value: $15-20.

Crêpe Paper Edition, Value: $3-5.

20. THE GOBLIN SPIDER. Japanese Fairy Tales. Second Series, No. 1. By Lafcadio Hearn. Tokyo, (1899).

Wrappers. Size 4⅞x7". Printed in colors by hand from wood blocks.

21. SAME: Printed on Crêpe-Paper, size 4x 5$\frac{15}{16}$". Description as above. Dated 10th April, 1899; publisher's address should be 10 Hiyoshicho, Kyobashi, Tokyo, NOT 38 Yotsuya Hommura, Tokyo.

Value: $15-20.

Crêpe-Paper Edition, Value: $3-5.

22. CLARIMONDE. Translated by Lafcadio
Hearn From the French of Theophile Gautier.
New York, (1899).

Bound in orange cloth, with blue lettering,
and decorations. First separate printing of this
story.

Value: $6-10.

1899

23. IN GHOSTLY JAPAN. Boston, 1899.
Decorated blue cloth binding.

Value: $7-12.

1900

24. SHADOWINGS. Boston, 1900.

Decorated blue cloth binding.

Value: $6-10.

25. A JAPANESE MISCELLANY. Boston, 1901.

Decorated green cloth binding.

Value: $7-10.

(1902)

26. THE OLD WOMAN WHO LOST HER DUMPLING. Japanese Fairy Tale Series No. 24. Rendered Into English by Lafcadio Hearn. (Tokyo, 1902).

Wrappers. Size $7\frac{3}{16}$x9½". Printed in colors by hand from wood blocks.

27. SAME: Printed on Crêpe-Paper, size $5\frac{7}{16}$x7½". Description same as above.

Value: $15-20.

Crêpe-Paper Edition, Value: $3-5.

28. KOTTO BEING JAPANESE CURIOS
WITH SUNDRY COBWEBS COLLECTED
BY LAFCADIO HEARN. New York, 1902.

Decorated olive-green cloth binding. First
issue copies have ornamental border on title page
printed upside down, with artist's monogram in
upper right instead of lower left.

Value: $10-12.

(1903)

29. CHIN CHIN KOBAKAMA. Japanese
Fairy Tale Series No. 25. Rendered Into English
By Lafcadio Hearn. (Tokyo, 1903).

Wrappers. Size $7\frac{1}{4}$x$9\frac{5}{16}$″. Printed in
colors by hand from wood blocks.

30. SAME: Printed on Crêpe-Paper, size
$5\frac{5}{16}$x$7\frac{1}{2}$″. Description as above. Should not
have Simpkin Marshall imprint in the copyright
notice.

Value: $15-20.

Crêpe-Paper Edition, Value: $3-5.

31. KWAIDAN: STORIES AND STUDIES
OF STRANGE THINGS. Boston and New
York, 1904.

Decorated blue-green binding. (Typographical design and supervision by Bruce
Rogers)

Value: $8-14.

1904

32. JAPAN AN ATTEMPT AT INTER-
PRETATION. New York, 1904.

Bound in light brown cloth.

Value: $7-12.

1905

33. THE ROMANCE OF THE MILKY
WAY AND OTHER STUDIES AND STO-
RIES. Boston and New York, 1905.

Bound in gray cloth with all-over yellow
stamping. Olive-green cloth used in later editions. (Typographical design and supervision by
Bruce Rogers.)

Value: $8-12.

34. THE LIFE AND LETTERS OF LAF-
CADIO HEARN. By Elizabeth Bisland. 2
volumes. Boston and New York, 1906.

Bound in dark green cloth with paper labels.
Limited to 200 copies, uncut. Original mss. page
inserted.

35. SAME: Trade edition in dark green cloth
with title and imprint stamped in gold on backbone.

Value: $60-75.

Trade Edition, Value: $7-10.

1907

36. LETTERS FROM THE RAVEN. Being
The Correspondence of Lafcadio Hearn with
Henry Watkin. New York, 1907.

Bound in brown boards with black cloth back.

Value: $3-5.

37. THE JAPANESE LETTERS OF LAF-
CADIO HEARN. By Elizabeth Bisland. Boston and New York, 1910.

Bound in dark green cloth with paper label.
Limited to 200 copies, uncut.

38. SAME: Trade edition in dark green cloth,
with title and imprint stamped in gold on backbone. (Uniform with "The Life & Letters")

Value: $6-8.

Trade Edition, Value: $3-4.

39. THE TEMPTATION OF ST.
ANTHONY. By Gustave Flaubert. Translated
by Lafcadio Hearn. New York and Seattle, 1910.

Bound in gray cloth with white lettering.
The 1911 (second) Edition of this work has
added material.

Value: $3-4.

40. LEAVES FROM THE DIARY OF AN IMPRESSIONIST. Boston and New York, 1911.

Bound in blue boards with yellow cloth back, with paper label. Boxed. Limited edition of 575 copies.

Value: $8-15.

(1913)

41. EDITORIALS FROM THE KOBE CHRONICLE. (New York, 1913) Privately printed.

Bound in white wrappers. Limited to 100 copies.

Value: $10-25.

1914

42. FANTASTICS AND OTHER FANCIES. Boston and New York, 1914.

Bound in blue boards with yellow cloth back with paper label. Boxed. Limited to 550 numbered copies. The Trade edition of this work was not published until 1919.

Value: $7-10.

43. JAPANESE LYRICS. Translated By Lafcadio Hearn. Boston and New York, 1915.

Bound in green wrappers. Title page pasted in on stub.

Value: $5-8.

44. INTERPRETATIONS OF LITERATURE. Edited by John Erskine. 2 volumes. New York, 1915.

Bound in red buckram with paper labels, gilt top.

Value: $4-7.

45. APPRECIATIONS OF POETRY. Edited by John Erskine. New York, 1916.

Bound in red cloth with paper label, gilt top.

Value: $3-5.

1917

46. LIFE AND LITERATURE. Edited by John Erskine. New York, 1917.

Bound in red cloth, with paper label, gilt top.

Value: $3-4.

1918

47. KARMA. New York, 1918.

Bound in blue boards with white cloth back, black lettering.

Value: $2-5.

1920

48. TALKS TO WRITERS. Edited by John Erskine. New York, 1920.

Bound in brown buckram.

Value: $2-4.

49. ON COMPOSITION. Atlantic Readings Number 13. By Lafcadio Hearn. Boston, (1920)

Bound in brown wrappers.

Value: $2-3.

(1921)

50. ON READING IN RELATION TO LITERATURE. Atlantic Readings Number 17. By Lafcadio Hearn. Boston, (1921)

Bound in brown wrappers.

Value: $2-3.

1921

51. BOOKS AND HABITS. Edited by John Erskine. New York, 1921.

Bound in red cloth, with paper label.

Value: $3-4.

52. THE DREAM OF A SUMMER DAY.
Boston and New York, 1922.

Bound in white wrappers. First separate
printing. (First book appearance, in "Out Of
The East".)

Value: $8-12.

53. PRE-RAPHAELITE AND OTHER
POETS. Edited by John Erskine. New York,
1922.

Bound in red cloth.

Value: $3-4.

54. THE FOUNTAIN OF YOUTH. Japanese Fairy Tale, Rendered Into English by Lafcadio Hearn. (Tokyo, 1922).

Wrappers: Size $7\frac{1}{16}$x$9\frac{9}{16}$". Printed in colors by hand from wood blocks.

55. SAME: Printed on Crêpe-Paper, size $5\frac{1}{2}$x $7\frac{1}{2}$". Description same as above.

Value: $15-20.

Crêpe-Paper Edition, Value $3-5.

1923

56. ESSAYS IN EUROPEAN AND ORIENTAL LITERATURE. Edited by Albert Mordell. New York, 1923.

Bound in red cloth, with paper label.

Value: $3-5.

57. KIMIKO AND OTHER JAPANESE SKETCHES. Boston and New York, 1923.

Bound in green boards. Published separately for the first time in the "Evergreen Series."

Value: $1-3.

58. CREOLE SKETCHES. Edited by Charles Woodward Hutson. Boston and New York, 1924.

Bound in red cloth. Most of the material in this volume first appeared in the Collected Writings of Hearn published in 16 volumes in 1922.

Value: $2-4.

59. AN AMERICAN MISCELLANY. Edited by Albert Mordell. 2 volumes. New York, 1924.

Bound in red cloth, paper labels. Boxed.

Value: $5-8.

60. SAINT ANTHONY AND OTHER STO-
RIES. By Guy de Maupassant. Selected and
Translated by Lafcadio Hearn. Edited by Albert
Mordell. New York, 1924.

Bound in deep red cloth.

Value: $3-4.

61. KUSA-HIBARI From The Book "Kotto".
Montreal, 1924. Limited to 350 copies; privately
printed by the Ronalds Company Ltd., for Christ-
mas.

Value: $

62. OCCIDENTAL GLEANINGS. Sketches
and Essays Now First Collected by Albert Mordell. 2 volumes. New York, 1925.

Bound in red cloth with paper labels.

Value: $5-7.

63. SOME NEW LETTERS AND WRIT-INGS OF LAFCADIO HEARN. Collected and Edited by Sanki Ichikawa. Tokyo, 1925.

Bound in black cloth, paper label, boxed.

Value: $3-5.

1926

64. EDITORIALS. Edited by Charles Wood-ward Hutson. Boston and New York, 1926.

Bound in green boards, cloth back, paper label. Limited edition of 250 copies.

65. SAME: Trade Edition, bound in greenish-brown cloth.

Value: $4-6.

Trade Edition, Value: $2-3.

1926

66. INSECTS AND GREEK POETRY. New York, 1926.

Bound in blue boards. Limited edition of 550 copies.

Value: $3-5.

67. A HISTORY OF ENGLISH LITERATURE. 2 volumes. Tokyo, 1927.

Bound in red cloth, boxed. A revised one volume edition of this work was published in 1930.

Value: $5-8.

(1927)

68. SOME STRANGE ENGLISH LITERARY FIGURES OF THE EIGHTEENTH AND NINETEENTH CENTURIES. Tokyo, (1927)

Bound in green cloth.

Value: $4-5.

1928

69. THE TALE OF A FAN. Chicago, 1928.

Brochure of 4 pages printed on single folded sheet. Separate printing, taken from "Fantastics." Privately printed for presentation by Targ's Bookshop.

Value: $1-2.

(1928)

70. LECTURES ON SHAKESPEARE.
Edited by Iwao Inagaki. Tokyo (1928)

Bound in dark green cloth.

Value: $2-3.

(1928)

71. ROMANCE AND REASON. Compiled
by R. Tanabe. Tokyo (1928).

Bound in light green cloth.

Value: $2-3.

(1929)

72. FACTS AND FANCIES. Edited by R.
Tanabe. Tokyo (1929).

Bound in pale green cloth.

Value: $2-3.

73. ESSAYS ON AMERICAN LITERA-
TURE. Edited by Sanki Ichikawa. Tokyo, 1929.

Bound in red cloth.

Value: $3-4.

(1929)

74. LECTURES ON PROSODY. (Tokyo,
1929)

Bound in green cloth.

Value: $2-3.

(1930)

75. VICTORIAN PHILOSOPHY. (Tokyo,
1930).

Bound in green cloth.

Value: $2-3.

76. WILLIAM COLLINS. By Ueda Bin. (Tokyo, 1930)

Wrappers. Limited edition of 300 copies of a facsimile MSS. showing corrections and critical notations in the hand of Lafcadio Hearn.

Value: $

(1931)

77. THE ADVENTURES OF WALTER SCHNAFFS AND OTHER STORIES. By Guy de Maupassant. Translated by Lafcadio Hearn. (Tokyo, 1931).

Bound in black cloth.

Value: $2-3.

(1932)

78. ON ART, LITERATURE AND PHILOSOPHY. Edited by Tyuji Tanabe. Tokyo (1932).

Bound in green cloth. Boxed.

Value: $3-5.

79. STORIES FROM PIERRE LOTI. Translated by Lafcadio Hearn. (Tokyo, 1933).

Bound in blue-black cloth.

Value: $2-3.

1933

80. GIBBETED: Execution Of A Youthful Murderer, etc. Los Angeles, 1933.

Black cloth binding, paper label on spine. Limited to 200 copies.

Value: $2-3.

1933

81. LETTERS TO A PAGAN. Detroit, 1933.

Bound in decorated boards, with gold cloth back, boxed. Limited edition of 500 copies.

Value: $6-7.

1934

82. LETTERS FROM SHIMANE AND KYUSHU. Kyoto, 1934.

Bound in rough reddish-brown cloth, boxed. Limited edition of 100 copies.

Value: $10-12.

1934

83. JAPANESE GOBLIN POETRY. Rendered Into English by Lafcadio Hearn and Illustrated from His Drawings. Compiled by his Son Kazuo Koizumi. Tokyo, 1934.

Folio. Blue cloth with paper labels. Limited edition of 500 copies. In folding box.

Value: $8-10.

BOOKS ABOUT LAFCADIO HEARN

BISLAND, Elizabeth. Life And Letters of Lafcadio Hearn. 2 volumes. N. Y. 1906. See Items, 34, 35.

GOULD, George M. Concerning Lafcadio Hearn. Philadelphia, (1908).

BISLAND, Elizabeth. The Japanese Letters of Lafcadio Hearn. New York, 1910. See Items, 37, 38.

NOGUCHI, Yone. Lafcadio Hearn In Japan. With Mrs. Lafcadio Hearn's Reminiscences. London and Yokohama, 1910.

KENNARD, Nina H. Lafcadio Hearn. Containing Some Letters From Lafcadio Hearn To His Half-sister Mrs. Atkinson. London, 1911.

THOMAS, Edward. Lafcadio Hearn. London, 1912.

KOIZUMI, Setsuko (Mrs. Hearn.)   Reminiscences of Lafcadio Hearn.   Boston, 1918.

TICKNOR, Caroline.   Glimpses Of Authors. Boston, 1922.   Chapter IX deals with Hearn and contains two letters to the author never before published.

TINKER, Edward Larocque.   Lafcadio Hearn's American Days.   N. Y. 1924.

BALL, Charles E. Lafcadio Hearn, An Appreciation.   London (1926).

HENDRICK, Ellwood.   Lafcadio Hearn.   New York, 1929.

LEWIS, Oscar.   Hearn And His Biographers. The Record of a Literary Controversy.   Together With A Group of Letters From Lafcadio Hearn To Joseph Tunison Now First Published.   San Francisco, 1930.

TEMPLE, Jean.   Blue Ghost, A Study of Lafcadio Hearn.   New York, (1931).

PERKINS, P. D. and Ione.   Lafcadio Hearn. A Bibliography of His Writings.   Boston, 1934.

BAREL, Leona Queyrouse. The Idyl. Tokyo, 1935.

KOIZUMI, Kazuo. Father And I. Memories of Lafcadio Hearn. Boston, 1935.

INDEX*

Books About Lafcadio Hearn not included in the above
Index. See Page 45.